This thoughtful journal helps children reflect on  them to listen for God's voice as they read, ins someone else's thoughts or explanations. A helpi. for Christian families!

— Christie Thomas, author of *Quinn's Promise Rock*

Taryn's *Reflective Bible Journal for Kids* is a valuable resource for families! I love how it teaches children that God is speaking to them personally through His word. It also helps kids identify their emotions, reflect on what God has done through the week, and take action to do one nice thing for someone else. This journal helps children practice connecting with God and implement what they are learning in His word.

— Sarah Keeling, author of *Psalm Prayers for Kids* and *Psalm Prayers for the Nations*

Taryn Nergaard's *Reflective Bible Journal for Kids* is a practical yet deeply meaningful journal that will help your child form lasting spiritual habits (to which all the parents said, AMEN!). Watch your child grow in connection, curiosity, and awe of the Lord as they use this child friendly journal! I'm so grateful to have this tool to use with my son.

— Kristin Vanderlip, author of *Living Life Well: A Daily Growth Journal for Kids*

# Reflective Bible Journal

## FOR KIDS

TARYN NERGAARD

 typewriter creative co.

typewriter
creative co.

you are loved

# Contents

# A Note for Parents & Caregivers

First, I want to commend you on your desire to help your child(ren) establish a love for Bible reading. Parenting is no easy task, and attending to their physical and emotional needs often requires all we have. I know that nurturing your child's spiritual needs can sometimes feel like more than you can handle.

As parents, we often have more questions than answers, so we wonder how we can adequately support our child's spiritual development. I want to let you off the hook a bit.

God already has a relationship with your child. He loves and cares for them. He speaks into their lives through whispers and gut feelings. **You get to show your child what is already true.**

As you help your child use the *Reflective Bible Journal for Kids*, you're empowering your child to recognize and develop their own personal relationship with God. They will learn how God's word is alive and active (Hebrews 4:12) and that the Holy Spirit is a trusted friend who helps them put the truths of the Bible into practice (John 14:16-17).

This is the foundation for a life-long journey of hearing God's voice and following his lead.

If you find this journal to be too simple for an older child, you may want to try the *Reflective Bible Journal for Teens*. It follows the same process, but with more challenging reflection questions. Choosing the right journal for your child will depend more on their emotional maturity and reading level, rather than age.

Additionally, one of the most effective ways to support your child's desire to develop their relationship with God is by modeling it yourself. The *Reflective Bible Journal: Hear God's Voice & Follow His Lead* is for adults at all stages of their faith journey. You will not only model the practice of daily Bible reading for your child, but you will also deepen your own ability to hear from the Holy Spirit, which will support your son or daughter when he/she has questions.

**I trust that God will honor your faithfulness as you seek to honor him in your family.**

# How to Use Your Journal

Monday to Friday:

1. Grab your Bible and a pen. **Open your journal to your "Daily Journal" pages.**

2. **Write the date in your journal.**

3. Think about how you're feeling right now and **record how you feel in your journal.**

4. **Choose a book of the Bible to read.** (*Hint: ask a parent or caregiver to help you pick somewhere to start.*)

5. Start at the beginning of the book or where you left off from last time and **choose one or more verses to read.** Only read as much as you can remember. You can always read more after you fill in your journal.

4. In your journal, **write down the verses you will read.** For example: Mark 1:1-2 or Luke 1:1-5.

5. In your Bible, **read the verses you chose and stop.** *Do you remember what you read?* If you don't, try reading it again. *Is there something you don't understand?* Ask your parent or caregiver for help.

6. If you remember and understand what you read, **close your eyes and ask God: What would you like me to know today?**

7. **Write down what you think you heard.** It's okay if you're not sure. Write it down anyway. If you don't think you heard anything, try closing your eyes again and listen. Or, write down what you already know about God. For example: God loves me. God made me. Jesus wants to be my friend forever.

> **A special note:** Every day is a new day to practice listening for God's voice. When Jesus went to heaven, he promised the disciples that he would send them a helper. He kept his promise and sent the Holy Spirit to be with the disciples. Anyone who loves God and follows Jesus also has the Holy Spirit as a helper. The Spirit comforts us, guides us, and speaks to us. The way the Holy Spirit speaks to us is different than the way we hear from our parents, siblings, and friends. The Spirit speaks more like a kind thought in your head or a warm feeling in your body.

After you've written down what you think God whispered to you through the Holy Spirit, it's time to pray and practice memorizing Bible verses.

8. **Finish the sentence: God, thank you for...**

9. **Finish the sentence: God, please help me...**

10. **Write down one of the memory verses on the next page or choose your own verse you want to remember.** You will write down the same memory verse every day until you can tell it to your parent or caregiver without looking.

11. **Draw a picture or doodle in the empty space.** God is our creator and he made us creative too.

## On the Weekend:

On the weekend you won't have a daily page to fill out in your journal. This is a great time to think about your week. **Use your "My Week" pages to help you remember and write down how you felt about your week.**

You'll also think about how you feel about next week.

If you feel worried, now is a great time to talk to your parent or caregiver so they can help you. And if you feel excited, tell them too so they can be happy with you!

I will ask the Father. And he will give you another friend to help you and to be with you forever. That friend is the Spirit of truth. The world can't accept him. That's because the world does not see him or know him. But you know him. He lives with you, and he will be in you.

John 14:16-17

# Memory Verses

## To remind us God loves us:

Psalm 86:15 - But Lord, you are a God who is tender and kind. You are gracious. You are slow to get angry. You are faithful and full of love.

Psalm 136:1 - Give thanks to the Lord, because he is good. His faithful love continues forever.

John 3:16 - God so loved the world that he gave his one and only Son. Anyone who believes in him will not die but will have eternal life.

Ephesians 2: 4 - But God loves us deeply. He is full of mercy.

1 Peter 5:7 - Turn all your worries over to him. He cares about you.

## To remind us to love others:

Proverbs 17:17 - A friend loves at all times. They are there to help when trouble comes.

1 Corinthians 13:13 - The three most important things to have are faith, hope and love. But the greatest of them is love.

1 Corinthians 16:14 - Be loving in everything you do.

1 John 3:16 - We know what love is because Jesus Christ gave his life for us. So we should give our lives for our brothers and sisters.

1 John 4:11 - Dear friends, since God loved us this much, we should also love one another.

# My Journal

Name:

_____

Age:

_____

Date: _____

I feel...   Happy   Sad   Angry   Lonely   Scared

Silly   Calm   Other: _____

Today I read: _____

What I think God wants me to know:

_____

_____

_____

_____

God, thank you for...

_____

_____

_____

God, please help me...

_____

_____

_____

# My Memory Verse

_____

_____

_____

_____

_____

Doodle & Drawing Space

Date: _____

I feel...    Happy    Sad    Angry    Lonely    Scared

Silly    Calm    Other: _____

Today I read: _____

What I think God wants me to know:

_____

_____

_____

_____

God, thank you for...

_____

_____

_____

God, please help me...

_____

_____

_____

# My Memory Verse

_____

_____

_____

_____

_____

Doodle & Drawing Space

Date: _____

I feel...    Happy    Sad    Angry    Lonely    Scared
         Silly    Calm    Other: _____

Today I read: _____

What I think God wants me to know:

_____

_____

_____

_____

God, thank you for...

_____

_____

_____

God, please help me...

_____

_____

_____

# My Memory Verse

_____

_____

_____

_____

_____

_____

Doodle & Drawing Space

Date: _____

I feel...    Happy    Sad    Angry    Lonely    Scared

         Silly    Calm    Other: _____

Today I read: _____

What I think God wants me to know:

_____

_____

_____

_____

God, thank you for...

_____

_____

_____

God, please help me...

_____

_____

_____

# My Memory Verse

_____

_____

_____

_____

_____

Doodle & Drawing Space

Date: _____

I feel...    Happy    Sad    Angry    Lonely    Scared

Silly    Calm    Other: _____

Today I read: _____

What I think God wants me to know:

_____

_____

_____

_____

God, thank you for...

_____

_____

_____

God, please help me...

_____

_____

_____

# My Memory Verse

_____

_____

_____

_____

_____

Doodle & Drawing Space

# My Week

The best part of my week was...

_____

_____

_____

_____

I was disappointed when...

_____

_____

_____

_____

I am grateful for...

_____

_____

_____

_____

The questions I have about God and what I read this week in my Bible are:

(Ask your mom, dad, or someone else who can help you find the answers.)

_____

_____

_____

_____

_____

I'm going to do something nice for: _____

I will:

_____

_____

_____

I'm excited about:

_____

_____

_____

Date: _____

I feel...    Happy    Sad    Angry    Lonely    Scared

Silly    Calm    Other: _____

Today I read: _____

What I think God wants me to know:

_____

_____

_____

_____

God, thank you for...

_____

_____

_____

God, please help me...

_____

_____

_____

# My Memory Verse

_____

_____

_____

_____

_____

Doodle & Drawing Space

Date: _____

I feel...     Happy     Sad     Angry     Lonely     Scared

        Silly     Calm     Other: _____

Today I read: _____

What I think God wants me to know:

_____

_____

_____

_____

God, thank you for...

_____

_____

_____

God, please help me...

_____

_____

_____

# My Memory Verse

_____

_____

_____

_____

_____

Doodle & Drawing Space

Date: _____

I feel...   Happy   Sad   Angry   Lonely   Scared
Silly   Calm   Other: _____

Today I read: _____

What I think God wants me to know:

_____

_____

_____

_____

God, thank you for...

_____

_____

_____

God, please help me...

_____

_____

_____

# My Memory Verse

_____

_____

_____

_____

_____

Doodle & Drawing Space

Date: _____

I feel...   Happy   Sad   Angry   Lonely   Scared
            Silly   Calm   Other: _____

Today I read: _____

What I think God wants me to know:

_____

_____

_____

_____

God, thank you for...

_____

_____

_____

God, please help me...

_____

_____

_____

# My Memory Verse

Doodle & Drawing Space

Date: _____

I feel...   Happy    Sad    Angry    Lonely    Scared

Silly    Calm    Other: _____

Today I read: _____

What I think God wants me to know:

_____

_____

_____

_____

God, thank you for...

_____

_____

_____

God, please help me...

_____

_____

_____

# My Memory Verse

_____

_____

_____

_____

_____

Doodle & Drawing Space

# My Week

The best part of my week was...

_____

_____

_____

I was disappointed when...

_____

_____

_____

I am grateful for...

_____

_____

_____

The questions I have about God and what I read this week in my Bible are:

(Ask your mom, dad, or someone else who can help you find the answers.)

_____

_____

_____

_____

_____

I'm going to do something nice for: _____

I will:

_____

_____

_____

I'm excited about:

_____

_____

_____

Date: _____

I feel...    Happy    Sad    Angry    Lonely    Scared
Silly    Calm    Other: _____

Today I read: _____

What I think God wants me to know:

_____

_____

_____

_____

God, thank you for...

_____

_____

_____

God, please help me...

_____

_____

_____

# My Memory Verse

_____

_____

_____

_____

_____

Doodle & Drawing Space

Date: _____

I feel...   Happy   Sad   Angry   Lonely   Scared
            Silly   Calm   Other: _____

Today I read: _____

What I think God wants me to know:

_____

_____

_____

_____

God, thank you for...

_____

_____

_____

God, please help me...

_____

_____

_____

# My Memory Verse

_____

_____

_____

_____

_____

_____

Doodle & Drawing Space

Date: _____

I feel...　Happy　Sad　Angry　Lonely　Scared
　　　　Silly　Calm　Other: _____

Today I read: _____

What I think God wants me to know:

_____

_____

_____

_____

God, thank you for...

_____

_____

God, please help me...

_____

_____

# My Memory Verse

_____

_____

_____

_____

_____

Doodle & Drawing Space

Date: _____

I feel...   Happy   Sad   Angry   Lonely   Scared
            Silly   Calm   Other: _____

Today I read: _____

What I think God wants me to know:

_____

_____

_____

_____

God, thank you for...

_____

_____

_____

God, please help me...

_____

_____

_____

# My Memory Verse

_____

_____

_____

_____

_____

Doodle & Drawing Space

Date: _____

I feel...    Happy    Sad    Angry    Lonely    Scared

Silly    Calm    Other: _____

Today I read: _____

What I think God wants me to know:

_____

_____

_____

_____

God, thank you for...

_____

_____

_____

God, please help me...

_____

_____

_____

# My Memory Verse

Doodle & Drawing Space

# My Week

The best part of my week was...

_____

_____

_____

_____

I was disappointed when...

_____

_____

_____

_____

I am grateful for...

_____

_____

_____

_____

The questions I have about God and what I read this week in my Bible are:

(Ask your mom, dad, or someone else who can help you find the answers.)

_____

_____

_____

_____

_____

I'm going to do something nice for: _____

I will:

_____

_____

_____

I'm excited about:

_____

_____

_____

Date: _____

I feel...　　Happy　　Sad　　Angry　　Lonely　　Scared

　　　　　　Silly　　Calm　　Other: _____

Today I read: _____

What I think God wants me to know:

_____

_____

_____

_____

God, thank you for...

_____

_____

_____

God, please help me...

_____

_____

_____

# My Memory Verse

_____

_____

_____

_____

_____

_____

Doodle & Drawing Space

Date: _____

I feel...    Happy    Sad    Angry    Lonely    Scared

Silly    Calm    Other: _____

Today I read: _____

What I think God wants me to know:

_____

_____

_____

_____

God, thank you for...

_____

_____

_____

God, please help me...

_____

_____

_____

# My Memory Verse

Doodle & Drawing Space

Date: _____

I feel...    Happy    Sad    Angry    Lonely    Scared
            Silly    Calm    Other: _____

Today I read: _____

What I think God wants me to know:

_____

_____

_____

_____

God, thank you for...

_____

_____

_____

God, please help me...

_____

_____

_____

# My Memory Verse

_____

_____

_____

_____

_____

Doodle & Drawing Space

Date: _____

I feel...   Happy   Sad   Angry   Lonely   Scared
         Silly   Calm   Other: _____

Today I read: _____

What I think God wants me to know:

_____

_____

_____

_____

God, thank you for...

_____

_____

_____

God, please help me...

_____

_____

_____

# My Memory Verse

_____

_____

_____

_____

_____

Doodle & Drawing Space

Date: _____

I feel...    Happy    Sad    Angry    Lonely    Scared

Silly    Calm    Other: _____

Today I read: _____

What I think God wants me to know:

_____

_____

_____

_____

God, thank you for...

_____

_____

_____

God, please help me...

_____

_____

_____

# My Memory Verse

_____

_____

_____

_____

_____

Doodle & Drawing Space

# My Week

The best part of my week was...

_____

_____

_____

_____

I was disappointed when...

_____

_____

_____

_____

I am grateful for...

_____

_____

_____

_____

The questions I have about God and what I read this week in my Bible are:

(Ask your mom, dad, or someone else who can help you find the answers.)

_____

_____

_____

_____

_____

I'm going to do something nice for: _____

I will:

_____

_____

_____

I'm excited about:

_____

_____

_____

Date: _____

I feel...    Happy    Sad    Angry    Lonely    Scared
             Silly    Calm    Other: _____

Today I read: _____

What I think God wants me to know:

_____

_____

_____

_____

God, thank you for...

_____

_____

_____

God, please help me...

_____

_____

_____

# My Memory Verse

_____

_____

_____

_____

_____

_____

Doodle & Drawing Space

Date: _____

I feel...   Happy    Sad    Angry    Lonely    Scared

Silly    Calm    Other: _____

Today I read: _____

What I think God wants me to know:

_____

_____

_____

_____

God, thank you for...

_____

_____

God, please help me...

_____

_____

_____

# My Memory Verse

_____

_____

_____

_____

_____

Doodle & Drawing Space

Date: _____

I feel...  Happy    Sad    Angry    Lonely    Scared
           Silly    Calm    Other: _____

Today I read: _____

What I think God wants me to know:

_____

_____

_____

_____

God, thank you for...

_____

_____

_____

God, please help me...

_____

_____

_____

# My Memory Verse

Doodle & Drawing Space

Date: _____

I feel...    Happy    Sad    Angry    Lonely    Scared
             Silly    Calm    Other: _____

Today I read: _____

What I think God wants me to know:

_____

_____

_____

_____

God, thank you for...

_____

_____

_____

God, please help me...

_____

_____

_____

# My Memory Verse

Doodle & Drawing Space

Date: _____

I feel...   Happy   Sad   Angry   Lonely   Scared   Silly   Calm   Other: _____

Today I read: _____

What I think God wants me to know:

_____

_____

_____

_____

God, thank you for...

_____

_____

_____

God, please help me...

_____

_____

_____

# My Memory Verse

Doodle & Drawing Space

# My Week

The best part of my week was...

_____

_____

_____

_____

I was disappointed when...

_____

_____

_____

_____

I am grateful for...

_____

_____

_____

_____

The questions I have about God and what I read this week
in my Bible are:

(Ask your mom, dad, or someone else who can help you find the answers.)

_____

_____

_____

_____

I'm going to do something nice for: _____

I will:

_____

_____

_____

I'm excited about:

_____

_____

_____

Date: _____

I feel...    Happy    Sad    Angry    Lonely    Scared

Silly    Calm    Other: _____

Today I read: _____

What I think God wants me to know:

_____

_____

_____

_____

God, thank you for...

_____

_____

_____

God, please help me...

_____

_____

_____

# My Memory Verse

_____

_____

_____

_____

_____

Doodle & Drawing Space

Date: _____

I feel...    Happy    Sad    Angry    Lonely    Scared
             Silly    Calm    Other: _____

Today I read: _____

What I think God wants me to know:

_____

_____

_____

_____

God, thank you for...

_____

_____

_____

God, please help me...

_____

_____

_____

# My Memory Verse

_____

_____

_____

_____

_____

_____

Doodle & Drawing Space

Date: _____

I feel...    Happy    Sad    Angry    Lonely    Scared
            Silly    Calm    Other: _____

Today I read: _____

What I think God wants me to know:

_____

_____

_____

_____

God, thank you for...

_____

_____

_____

God, please help me...

_____

_____

_____

# My Memory Verse

Doodle & Drawing Space

Date: _____

I feel...    Happy    Sad    Angry    Lonely    Scared
             Silly    Calm    Other: _____

Today I read: _____

What I think God wants me to know:

_____

_____

_____

_____

God, thank you for...

_____

_____

_____

God, please help me...

_____

_____

_____

# My Memory Verse

_____

_____

_____

_____

_____

Doodle & Drawing Space

Date: _____

I feel...    Happy    Sad    Angry    Lonely    Scared    Silly    Calm    Other: _____

Today I read: _____

What I think God wants me to know:

_____

_____

_____

_____

God, thank you for...

_____

_____

_____

God, please help me...

_____

_____

_____

# My Memory Verse

_____

_____

_____

_____

_____

_____

Doodle & Drawing Space

# My Week

The best part of my week was...

_____

_____

_____

_____

I was disappointed when...

_____

_____

_____

_____

I am grateful for...

_____

_____

_____

_____

The questions I have about God and what I read this week
in my Bible are:

(Ask your mom, dad, or someone else who can help you find the answers.)

_____

_____

_____

_____

I'm going to do something nice for: _____

I will:

_____

_____

_____

I'm excited about:

_____

_____

_____

Date: _____

I feel...   Happy   Sad   Angry   Lonely   Scared
            Silly   Calm   Other: _____

Today I read: _____

What I think God wants me to know:

_____

_____

_____

_____

God, thank you for...

_____

_____

_____

God, please help me...

_____

_____

_____

# My Memory Verse

_____

_____

_____

_____

_____

Doodle & Drawing Space

Date: _____

I feel...   Happy     Sad    Angry    Lonely    Scared
            Silly    Calm    Other: _____

Today I read: _____

What I think God wants me to know:

_____

_____

_____

_____

God, thank you for...

_____

_____

_____

God, please help me...

_____

_____

_____

# My Memory Verse

Doodle & Drawing Space

Date: _____

I feel...    Happy     Sad    Angry    Lonely    Scared

Silly    Calm    Other: _____

Today I read: _____

What I think God wants me to know:

_____

_____

_____

_____

God, thank you for...

_____

_____

_____

God, please help me...

_____

_____

_____

# My Memory Verse

_____

_____

_____

_____

_____

Doodle & Drawing Space

Date: _____

I feel...    Happy    Sad    Angry    Lonely    Scared
             Silly    Calm    Other: _____

Today I read: _____

What I think God wants me to know:

_____

_____

_____

_____

God, thank you for...

_____

_____

_____

God, please help me...

_____

_____

_____

# My Memory Verse

Doodle & Drawing Space

Date: _____

I feel...    Happy    Sad    Angry    Lonely    Scared
             Silly    Calm    Other: _____

Today I read: _____

What I think God wants me to know:

_____

_____

_____

_____

God, thank you for...

_____

_____

_____

God, please help me...

_____

_____

_____

# My Memory Verse

Doodle & Drawing Space

# My Week

The best part of my week was...

_____

_____

_____

_____

I was disappointed when...

_____

_____

_____

_____

I am grateful for...

_____

_____

_____

_____

The questions I have about God and what I read this week
in my Bible are:

(Ask your mom, dad, or someone else who can help you find the answers.)

_____

_____

_____

_____

_____

I'm going to do something nice for: _____

I will:

_____

_____

_____

I'm excited about:

_____

_____

_____

Date: _____

I feel...    Happy     Sad     Angry     Lonely     Scared

Silly     Calm     Other: _____

Today I read: _____

What I think God wants me to know:

_____

_____

_____

_____

God, thank you for...

_____

_____

_____

God, please help me...

_____

_____

_____

# My Memory Verse

_____

_____

_____

_____

_____

_____

Doodle & Drawing Space

Date: _____

I feel...    Happy    Sad    Angry    Lonely    Scared
Silly    Calm    Other: _____

Today I read: _____

What I think God wants me to know:

_____

_____

_____

_____

God, thank you for...

_____

_____

_____

God, please help me...

_____

_____

_____

# My Memory Verse

_____

_____

_____

_____

_____

_____

Doodle & Drawing Space

Date: _____

I feel...    Happy    Sad    Angry    Lonely    Scared
             Silly    Calm    Other: _____

Today I read: _____

What I think God wants me to know:

_____

_____

_____

_____

God, thank you for...

_____

_____

_____

God, please help me...

_____

_____

_____

# My Memory Verse

Doodle & Drawing Space

Date: _____

I feel...  Happy    Sad   Angry   Lonely   Scared

Silly   Calm   Other: _____

Today I read: _____

What I think God wants me to know:

_____

_____

_____

_____

God, thank you for...

_____

_____

_____

God, please help me...

_____

_____

_____

# My Memory Verse

_____

_____

_____

_____

_____

Doodle & Drawing Space

Date: _____

I feel...   Happy    Sad    Angry    Lonely    Scared

Silly    Calm    Other: _____

Today I read: _____

What I think God wants me to know:

_____

_____

_____

_____

God, thank you for...

_____

_____

_____

God, please help me...

_____

_____

_____

# My Memory Verse

_____

_____

_____

_____

_____

Doodle & Drawing Space

# My Week

The best part of my week was...

_____

_____

_____

_____

I was disappointed when...

_____

_____

_____

I am grateful for...

_____

_____

_____

_____

The questions I have about God and what I read this week
in my Bible are:

(Ask your mom, dad, or someone else who can help you find the answers.)

_____

_____

_____

_____

I'm going to do something nice for: _____

I will:

_____

_____

_____

I'm excited about:

_____

_____

_____

Date: _____

I feel...    Happy    Sad    Angry    Lonely    Scared    Silly    Calm    Other: _____

Today I read: _____

What I think God wants me to know:

_____

_____

_____

_____

God, thank you for...

_____

_____

_____

God, please help me...

_____

_____

_____

# My Memory Verse

_____

_____

_____

_____

_____

Doodle & Drawing Space

Date: _____

I feel...    Happy    Sad    Angry    Lonely    Scared
             Silly    Calm    Other: _____

Today I read: _____

What I think God wants me to know:

_____

_____

_____

_____

God, thank you for...

_____

_____

_____

God, please help me...

_____

_____

_____

# My Memory Verse

Doodle & Drawing Space

Date: _____

I feel...    Happy     Sad    Angry    Lonely    Scared
             Silly    Calm    Other: _____

Today I read: _____

What I think God wants me to know:

_____

_____

_____

_____

God, thank you for...

_____

_____

_____

God, please help me...

_____

_____

_____

# My Memory Verse

_____

_____

_____

_____

_____

Doodle & Drawing Space

Date: _____

I feel...    Happy    Sad    Angry    Lonely    Scared
             Silly    Calm    Other: _____

Today I read: _____

What I think God wants me to know:

_____

_____

_____

_____

God, thank you for...

_____

_____

_____

God, please help me...

_____

_____

_____

# My Memory Verse

Doodle & Drawing Space

Date: _____

I feel...    Happy    Sad    Angry    Lonely    Scared

Silly    Calm    Other: _____

Today I read: _____

What I think God wants me to know:

_____

_____

_____

_____

God, thank you for...

_____

_____

_____

God, please help me...

_____

_____

_____

# My Memory Verse

Doodle & Drawing Space

# My Week

The best part of my week was...

_____

_____

_____

_____

I was disappointed when...

_____

_____

_____

_____

I am grateful for...

_____

_____

_____

_____

The questions I have about God and what I read this week
in my Bible are:

(Ask your mom, dad, or someone else who can help you find the answers.)

_____

_____

_____

_____

_____

I'm going to do something nice for: _____

I will:

_____

_____

_____

I'm excited about:

_____

_____

_____

Date: _____

I feel...    Happy    Sad    Angry    Lonely    Scared

Silly    Calm    Other: _____

Today I read: _____

What I think God wants me to know:

_____

_____

_____

_____

God, thank you for...

_____

_____

_____

God, please help me...

_____

_____

_____

# My Memory Verse

_____

_____

_____

_____

_____

Doodle & Drawing Space

Date: _____

I feel...    Happy    Sad    Angry    Lonely    Scared
            Silly    Calm    Other: _____

Today I read: _____

What I think God wants me to know:

_____

_____

_____

_____

God, thank you for...

_____

_____

_____

God, please help me...

_____

_____

_____

# My Memory Verse

_____

_____

_____

_____

_____

_____

Doodle & Drawing Space

Date: _____

I feel...    Happy    Sad    Angry    Lonely    Scared
Silly    Calm    Other: _____

Today I read: _____

What I think God wants me to know:

_____

_____

_____

_____

God, thank you for...

_____

_____

_____

God, please help me...

_____

_____

_____

# My Memory Verse

Doodle & Drawing Space

Date: _____

I feel...    Happy    Sad    Angry    Lonely    Scared

Silly    Calm    Other: _____

Today I read: _____

What I think God wants me to know:

_____

_____

_____

_____

God, thank you for...

_____

_____

_____

God, please help me...

_____

_____

_____

# My Memory Verse

_____

_____

_____

_____

_____

_____

Doodle & Drawing Space

Date: _____

I feel...    Happy    Sad    Angry    Lonely    Scared
             Silly    Calm    Other: _____

Today I read: _____

What I think God wants me to know:

_____

_____

_____

_____

God, thank you for...

_____

_____

_____

God, please help me...

_____

_____

_____

# My Memory Verse

Doodle & Drawing Space

# My Week

The best part of my week was...

_____

_____

_____

_____

I was disappointed when...

_____

_____

_____

_____

I am grateful for...

_____

_____

_____

_____

The questions I have about God and what I read this week
in my Bible are:

(Ask your mom, dad, or someone else who can help you find the answers.)

_____

_____

_____

_____

_____

I'm going to do something nice for: _____

I will:

_____

_____

_____

I'm excited about:

_____

_____

_____

Date: _____

I feel...   Happy    Sad    Angry    Lonely    Scared
           Silly    Calm    Other: _____

Today I read: _____

What I think God wants me to know:

_____

_____

_____

_____

God, thank you for...

_____

_____

_____

God, please help me...

_____

_____

_____

# My Memory Verse

_____

_____

_____

_____

_____

Doodle & Drawing Space

Date: _____

I feel...   Happy   Sad   Angry   Lonely   Scared
Silly   Calm   Other: _____

Today I read: _____

What I think God wants me to know:

_____

_____

_____

_____

God, thank you for...

_____

_____

_____

God, please help me...

_____

_____

_____

# My Memory Verse

_____

_____

_____

_____

_____

Doodle & Drawing Space

Date: _____

I feel...    Happy    Sad    Angry    Lonely    Scared
             Silly    Calm    Other: _____

Today I read: _____

What I think God wants me to know:

_____

_____

_____

_____

God, thank you for...

_____

_____

_____

God, please help me...

_____

_____

_____

# My Memory Verse

Doodle & Drawing Space

Date: _____

I feel...    Happy    Sad    Angry    Lonely    Scared
         Silly    Calm    Other: _____

Today I read: _____

What I think God wants me to know:

_____

_____

_____

_____

God, thank you for...

_____

_____

_____

God, please help me...

_____

_____

_____

# My Memory Verse

Doodle & Drawing Space

Date: _____

I feel...    Happy    Sad    Angry    Lonely    Scared

Silly    Calm    Other: _____

Today I read: _____

What I think God wants me to know:

_____

_____

_____

_____

God, thank you for...

_____

_____

_____

God, please help me...

_____

_____

_____

# My Memory Verse

Doodle & Drawing Space

# My Week

The best part of my week was...

_____

_____

_____

_____

I was disappointed when...

_____

_____

_____

_____

I am grateful for...

_____

_____

_____

_____

The questions I have about God and what I read this week
in my Bible are:

(Ask your mom, dad, or someone else who can help you find the answers.)

_____

_____

_____

_____

_____

I'm going to do something nice for: _____

I will:

_____

_____

_____

I'm excited about:

_____

_____

_____

Date: _____

I feel...    Happy    Sad    Angry    Lonely    Scared

Silly    Calm    Other: _____

Today I read: _____

What I think God wants me to know:

_____

_____

_____

_____

God, thank you for...

_____

_____

_____

God, please help me...

_____

_____

_____

# My Memory Verse

Doodle & Drawing Space

Date: _____

I feel...   Happy    Sad    Angry    Lonely    Scared
          Silly    Calm    Other: _____

Today I read: _____

What I think God wants me to know:

_____

_____

_____

_____

God, thank you for...

_____

_____

_____

God, please help me...

_____

_____

_____

# My Memory Verse

Doodle & Drawing Space

Date: _____

I feel...    Happy    Sad    Angry    Lonely    Scared

Silly    Calm    Other: _____

Today I read: _____

What I think God wants me to know:

_____

_____

_____

_____

God, thank you for...

_____

_____

_____

God, please help me...

_____

_____

_____

# My Memory Verse

Doodle & Drawing Space

Date: _____

I feel...    Happy    Sad    Angry    Lonely    Scared
             Silly    Calm    Other: _____

Today I read: _____

What I think God wants me to know:

_____

_____

_____

_____

God, thank you for...

_____

_____

_____

God, please help me...

_____

_____

_____

# My Memory Verse

_____

_____

_____

_____

_____

Doodle & Drawing Space

Date: _____

I feel...   Happy    Sad    Angry    Lonely    Scared

Silly    Calm    Other: _____

Today I read: _____

What I think God wants me to know:

_____

_____

_____

_____

God, thank you for...

_____

_____

_____

God, please help me...

_____

_____

_____

# My Memory Verse

_____

_____

_____

_____

_____

Doodle & Drawing Space

# My Week

The best part of my week was...

_____

_____

_____

_____

I was disappointed when...

_____

_____

_____

_____

I am grateful for...

_____

_____

_____

_____

The questions I have about God and what I read this week
in my Bible are:

(Ask your mom, dad, or someone else who can help you find the answers.)

_____

_____

_____

_____

_____

I'm going to do something nice for: _____

I will:

_____

_____

_____

I'm excited about:

_____

_____

_____

Date: _____

I feel...    Happy    Sad    Angry    Lonely    Scared
             Silly    Calm    Other: _____

Today I read: _____

What I think God wants me to know:

_____

_____

_____

_____

God, thank you for...

_____

_____

God, please help me...

_____

_____

# My Memory Verse

Doodle & Drawing Space

Date: _____

I feel...    Happy    Sad    Angry    Lonely    Scared
Silly    Calm    Other: _____

Today I read: _____

What I think God wants me to know:

_____

_____

_____

_____

God, thank you for...

_____

_____

_____

God, please help me...

_____

_____

_____

# My Memory Verse

Doodle & Drawing Space

Date: _____

I feel...  Happy   Sad   Angry   Lonely   Scared
          Silly   Calm   Other: _____

Today I read: _____

What I think God wants me to know:

_____

_____

_____

_____

God, thank you for...

_____

_____

_____

God, please help me...

_____

_____

_____

# My Memory Verse

Doodle & Drawing Space

Date: _____

I feel...    Happy    Sad    Angry    Lonely    Scared

Silly    Calm    Other: _____

Today I read: _____

What I think God wants me to know:

_____

_____

_____

_____

God, thank you for...

_____

_____

_____

God, please help me...

_____

_____

_____

# My Memory Verse

Doodle & Drawing Space

Date: _____

I feel...    Happy    Sad    Angry    Lonely    Scared

Silly    Calm    Other: _____

Today I read: _____

What I think God wants me to know:

_____

_____

_____

_____

God, thank you for...

_____

_____

_____

God, please help me...

_____

_____

_____

# My Memory Verse

Doodle & Drawing Space

# My Week

The best part of my week was...

_____

_____

_____

_____

I was disappointed when...

_____

_____

_____

_____

I am grateful for...

_____

_____

_____

_____

The questions I have about God and what I read this week in my Bible are:

(Ask your mom, dad, or someone else who can help you find the answers.)

_____

_____

_____

_____

_____

I'm going to do something nice for: _____

I will:

_____

_____

_____

I'm excited about:

_____

_____

_____

# Great job!

I completed my journal on:

_____

# Acknowledgments

This journal you hold has the power to transform your relationship with God. That's worth celebrating! So first I want to acknowledge you and the commitment you made to meet regularly with God.

In addition to my gratitude to God for every bit of grace and truth he has spoken into my life, I would like to thank the many others who took part in this work with me.

To the talented team who helped me with all the things that stressed me out: Jennie Scott, Katy Epling, and Sara Ward. Thank you for using your gifts for this project.

A special thank you to my writing mastermind: Cyndee Ownbey, Eva Kubasiak, Jazmin Frank, Katy Epling, Kristin Vanderlip, Sara Ward, and Thelma Nienhuis. Your presence makes this work less lonely and inspires me to keep going.

Thanks also to my extended writing community of hope*writers who supported me through endorsing and sharing this journal. And thank you to my early readers who provided such valuable feedback and helped shape these journals into what they are today.

My beautiful, kind, life-giving kids: Emery, Mia, Tessa, and Lincoln. You teach me every day what it means to love as Jesus does. These journals are for you. May they draw you closer to God and allow the Holy Spirit to comfort, guide, and encourage you no matter what you face in the years to come.

Finally, to my husband, Tynan. For a writer who can string sentences together for a living, words fail me in my deep love for you. I choose you every day.

# About the Author

Taryn Nergaard is an author and life coach with a passion for helping people find freedom. She is the creator of the *Reflective Bible Journals*, which help kids, teens, and adults hear God's voice and follow his lead. In her years leading a healing-discipleship ministry, she discovered that very few people know what true freedom in Christ feels like. She wants to change that. Taryn believes that surrender is the pathway to freedom, and when we stop holding on to what's holding us back, we experience more hope, joy, peace, and purpose.

Taryn lives in British Columbia, Canada with her husband and four kids. When she's not busy homeschooling or working, you'll find her enjoying a cup of coffee and a good book, or curled up on the couch binge watching her current favorite show.

@tarynnergaard
www.tarynnergaard.com

Made in the USA
Monee, IL
10 December 2020